Katie Tait Clifford

# Practise Your Phonics W
# Julia Donaldson's Songbirds

# OXFORD
## UNIVERSITY PRESS

# OXFORD
## UNIVERSITY PRESS

Great Clarendon Street, Oxford, OX2 6DP, United Kingdom

Oxford University Press is a department of the University of Oxford.
It furthers the University's objective of excellence in research, scholarship
and education by publishing worldwide. Oxford is a registered trade mark
of Oxford University Press in the UK and in certain other countries

First Edition published 2006
This Edition published 2012

British Library Cataloguing in Publication Data
Data available

978-0-19-279301-0

10 9 8 7 6 5 4 3

Printed in China

Paper used in the production of this book is a natural, recyclable product
made from wood grown in sustainable forests. The manufacturing process
conforms to the environmental regulations of the country of origin.

**Acknowledgements**
Series editor Clare Kirtley
Art edited by Hilary Wright

Help your child's learning
with essential tips, phonics
support and free eBooks
www.oxfordowl.co.uk

# Songbirds

# Queen Anneena's Feast

Story by Julia Donaldson
Pictures by Melanie Williamson
Series editor Clare Kirtley

## OXFORD
### UNIVERSITY PRESS

3

# Tips for reading Queen Anneena's Feast together

This book practises these letter patterns that all make the same sound:

ee   ea   y   e

Ask your child to point to these letter patterns and say the sound (e.g. *ee* as in *Queen*). Look out for these letter patterns in the story.

Your child might find these words tricky:

to   the   you   my   no   was   came
do   going   have   home   one
some   said   there   want   what

These words are common, but your child may not be able to sound them out yet. Say the words for your child if they do not know them.

Before you begin, ask your child to read the title. Remind your child to read words they do not recognise by sounding out and blending. Look at the picture together. What do you think this story is about?

When you have finished reading the story, look through it again and:

- Ask your child, *Why didn't Queen Teeny Weeny eat at the beginning of the story?* (She only wanted to eat one green leaf.)

- On page 16, find and read some words which contain a long *ee* sound (*clean, teeth*). Point to the letter pattern that makes the long *ee* sound in the words. Think of other words which contain long *ee* sounds (e.g. *leaf, seat, feet, been*).

Queen Anneena had a feast.

# Fifteen queens came to the feast.

# Queen Jean had heaps of meat.

Queen Nelly had heaps of jelly.

But Queen Teeny Weeny did not eat.

"Have some peas and beans," said Queen Jean.

"No," said Queen Teeny Weeny.

"Have some jelly and cream," said Queen Nelly.

"No," said Queen Teeny Weeny.

"What do you want to eat then?"
said Queen Anneena.

"One green leaf," said
Queen Teeny Weeny. But there
was not a leaf to be seen!

Queen Anneena sent King Kareem to the shop.

He came back with one green leaf.

Queen Anneena was happy to see Queen Teeny Weeny eat the leaf. "Do you want some tea and a sweet?" she said.

"No," said Queen Teeny Weeny.

19

"I am going home to clean my teeth."

# Songbirds

# Spike Says

Story by Julia Donaldson

Pictures by Teresa Murfin

Series editor Clare Kirtley

## OXFORD
### UNIVERSITY PRESS

# Tips for reading Spike Says together

This book practises these letter patterns that all make the same sound:

igh   y   ie   i-e   i

Ask your child to point to these letter patterns and say the sound (*i–e* as in *Spike*). Look out for these letter patterns in the story.

Your child might find these words tricky:

my   no   the   to   you   was   came
do   going   have   home   one
some   said   there   want   what

These words are common, but your child may not be able to sound them out yet. Say the words for your child if they do not know them.

Before you begin, ask your child to read the title. Remind your child to read words they do not recognise by sounding out and blending. Look at the picture together. What do you think this story is about?

When you have finished reading the story, look through it again and:

- Ask your child, *Which of Spike's claims do you like best? Why?*
- Find and read some words on pages 37 and 38 which contain a long *ie* sound (*pie, sky, night, Spike, lie*). Point to the letter pattern that makes the long *ie* sound in the word (*ie, y, igh, i–consonant–e, ie*). Think of other words which contain the long *ie* sound (e.g. *light, my, cry, like*).

Spike is five.

# Spike says he can run for miles

and miles.

Spike says he has nine bikes.

6

7

5

8

9

27

# Spike says he can dive.

He says he wins prizes for diving.

Spike says he can drive.

He says he wins prizes for driving.

# Spike says he can fight fires

and feed wild lions.

# Spike says his mum is a spy

and his dad rides a crocodile.

Spike says he can fly.

He says he eats a pie in the sky every night.

Spike says that he never, ever tells a lie.

# Songbirds

# The Wrong Kind of Knight

Story by Julia Donaldson
Pictures by Melanie Williamson
Series editor Clare Kirtley

**OXFORD**
UNIVERSITY PRESS

# Tips for reading The Wrong Kind of Knight together

This book practises these letter patterns:

> ee  ea  e  y  (all pronounced *ee* as in *three*)
>
> ie  i-e  igh  i  y  (all pronounced *ie* as in *tie*)
>
> n  kn  (pronounced *n* as in *not*)
>
> r  wr  (pronounced *r* as in *ran*)

Ask your child to point to these letter patterns and say the sounds (e.g. *n* as in *not*). Look out for these letter patterns in the story.

Your child might find these words tricky:

> the  to  too  you  no  was  never  knickers  don't
>
> door  liked  one  said  saw  some  there  were

These words are common, but your child may not be able to sound them out yet. Say the words for your child if they do not know them.

Before you begin, ask your child to read the title. Remind your child to read words they do not recognise by sounding out and blending. Look at the picture together. What do you think this story is about?

When you have finished reading the story, look through it again and:

- Ask your child, *Was Nasim the wrong kind of knight? Why?* (No, because he got rid of the dragon.)
- Find and read some words on page 53 which begin with an *n* sound (*no, knight, Nasim, knit*). Point to the letter patterns that make the *n* sound (*n, kn*).

Nasim was a knight.

But he didn't like to ride and he didn't like to fight.

Nasim liked to read and write, and he liked to knit.

One night, there was a knock at the door.

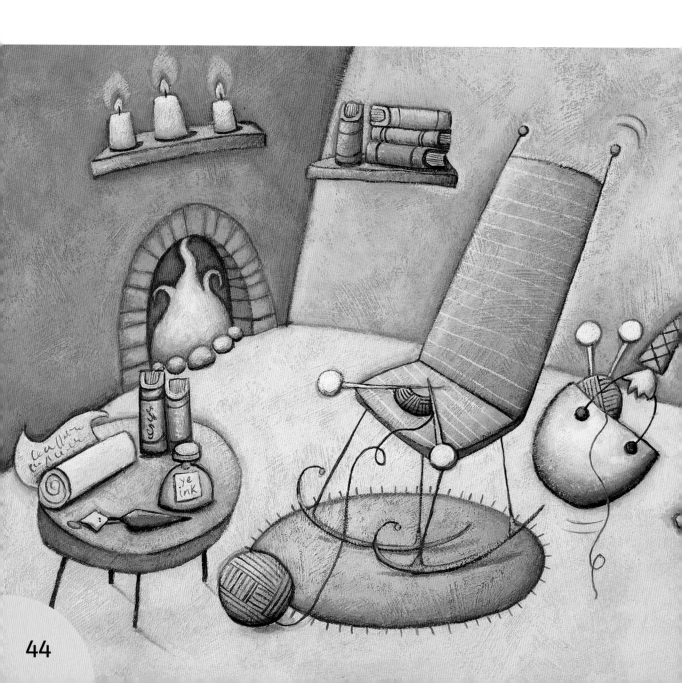

"I need you to fight a dragon!"
cried King Kareem.

"But I'm the wrong kind of knight!" said Nasim. "I don't like fighting!"

"Never mind!" cried the king.
"Hurry up!"

"The dragon is in my bed!" said the king.

Nasim's knees were knocking.
He lifted the blanket and saw ...

a tiny dragon.

The dragon's knees were
knocking too.
"I'm freezing," he said.

"Fight him!" cried the king.

"No. I'm the wrong kind of knight," said Nasim, and he began to knit.

Nasim was very quick at knitting. He knitted a vest, some socks and some long knickers.

The dragon was delighted.
"Thank you!" he said, and off
he went.

"I think you were the right kind of knight!" said the king.

# Songbirds

# Moan, Moan, Moan!

Story by Julia Donaldson

Pictures by Barbara Vagnozzi

Series editor Clare Kirtley

OXFORD
UNIVERSITY PRESS

# Tips for reading Moan, Moan, Moan! together

This book practises these letter patterns that all make the same sound:

oa    ow    o–e    o

Ask your child to point to these letter patterns and say the sound (*oa* as in *moan*). Look out for these letter patterns in the story.

Your child might find these words tricky:

climb   come   never   says   sister's
thumb   to   was   you   your

These words are common, but your child may not be able to sound them out yet. Say the words for your child if they do not know them.

Before you begin, ask your child to read the title. Remind your child to read words they do not recognise by sounding out and blending. Look at the picture together. What do you think this story is about?

When you have finished reading the story, look through it again and:

- Ask your child, *Why did the child wish her goldfish was her mum?* (Because her goldfish never moans.)

- Read pages 60 and 61, and find some words which contain a long *oe* sound (*don't, throw, stones, moans*). Point to the letter pattern that makes the long *oe* sound in the words (*o, ow, o–consonant–e, oa*). Find and read some more words which contain the letter pattern *oa* (*coat, soap, coal, slowcoach, toast, road*).

My goldfish never moans at me.
She never says,
"Don't climb that tree."

She never tells me,
"Don't throw stones."

But Mum just moans
and moans and moans.

64

67

68

69

I wish my goldfish was my mum.

# Songbirds

# The Snake and the Drake

Story by Julia Donaldson

Pictures by Jenny Williams

Series editor Clare Kirtley

## OXFORD
### UNIVERSITY PRESS

# Tips for reading The Snake and the Drake together

This book practises these letter patterns that all make the same sound:

**ai    ay    a-e    a**

Ask your child to point to these letter patterns and say the sound (*ai* as in *rainy*). Look out for these letter patterns in the story.

Your child might find these words tricky:

**can't   come   every   one   the   to   said   some   what   you**

These words are common, but your child may not be able to sound them out yet. Say the words for your child if they do not know them.

Before you begin, ask your child to read the title. Remind your child to read words they do not recognise by sounding out and blending. Look at the picture together. What do you think this story is about?

When you have finished reading the story, look through it again and:

- Ask your child, *Why did the snake let the drake get away?* (He thought the drake would bring him some yummy cake.)

- Read page 78, find some words which contain a long *ai* sound (*rainy, day, a, snake, came*). Point to the letter pattern that makes the long *ai* sound in the words (*ai, ay, a, a–consonant–e*). Find and read some more words which contain the letter pattern *ay* (*away, way, okay, lay*).

A duck and a drake had a
nest by a lake.

One rainy day, a snake
came to the nest.

The duck got away but the snake got the drake.

"Let go of my tail," said the drake.
"No," said the snake. "I am going
to eat you."

"Will you eat me with some cake?" said the drake. "That is the best way to eat drake."

"I can't make cake," said the snake.

"But Raven can make cake," said the drake.

"Raven's cake is yummy," said the drake.

"He makes it every day."

"What is in Raven's cake?" said the snake.

"Grapes and dates and raisins," said the drake.

"Yum yum," said the snake. "What a shame I can't fly to Raven's nest."

"But I can fly," said the drake.
"If you wait, I can get you some of
Raven's yummy cake."

"Okay. I will wait," said the snake, and he let the drake get away.

Snake lay and waited. He waited all day. But the drake did not come back.

Snake is still waiting.

# Songbirds

# Tadpoles

Story by Julia Donaldson
Pictures by Susie Thomas
Series editor Clare Kirtley

## OXFORD
UNIVERSITY PRESS

# Tips for reading Tadpoles together

This book practises these letter patterns:

> ee  ea  y  e  (all pronounced *ee* as in *three*)
>
> i–e  i  (all  pronounced *ie* as in *tie*)
>
> ow  o–e  o  (all pronounced *oe* as in *toe*)
>
> ai  ay  a–e  a  (all pronounced *ai* as in *train*)

Ask your child to point to these letter patterns and say the sounds (e.g. *ee* as in *three*). Look out for these letter patterns in the story.

Your child might find these words tricky:

> all  are  comes  have  here  out  some  these  they  the  to
>
> what  you

These words are common, but your child may not be able to sound them out yet. Say the words for your child if they do not know them.

Before you begin, ask your child to read the title. Remind your child to read words they do not recognise by sounding out and blending. Look at the picture together. What do you think this story is about?

When you have finished reading the story, look through it again and:

- Ask your child, *How does the tadpole change as it turns into a frog?* (It grows back legs, then front legs. It loses its tail.)
- Find and read some more words on page 97 which contain a long vowel sound (*grow, jelly*). Point to the letter pattern that makes the long vowel sound in these words (*ow, y*). Find and read some more words which contain a long *oe* sound (*those, growing, tadpoles, tadpole, only, no*).

What can you see in this lake?
Can you see some blobs of jelly?

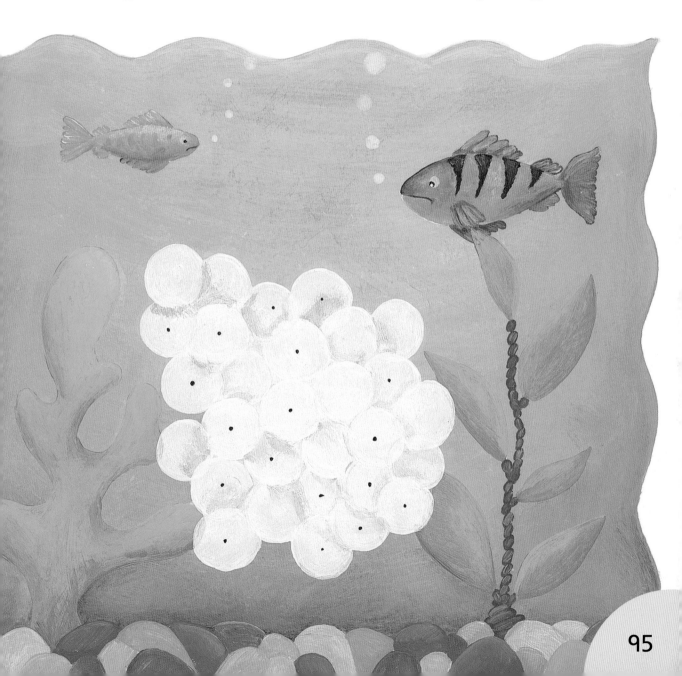

Can you see some black dots inside the jelly? Those dots are tiny eggs.

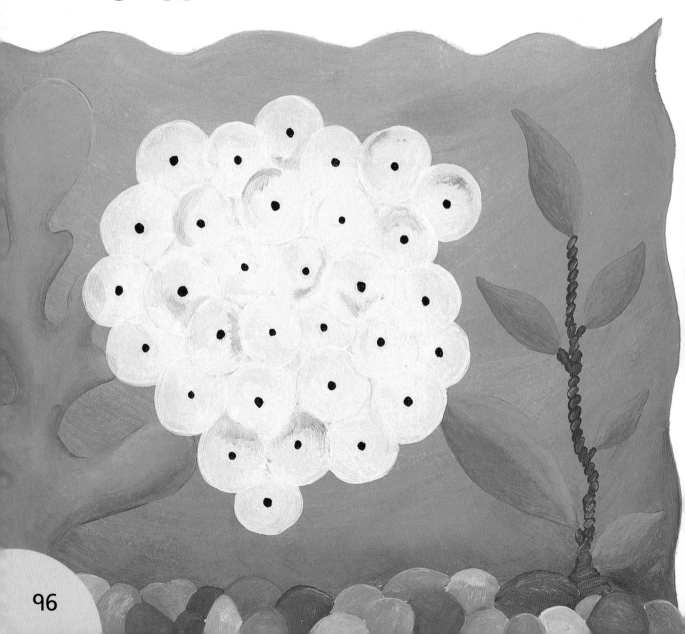

The dots grow. The jelly shrinks.

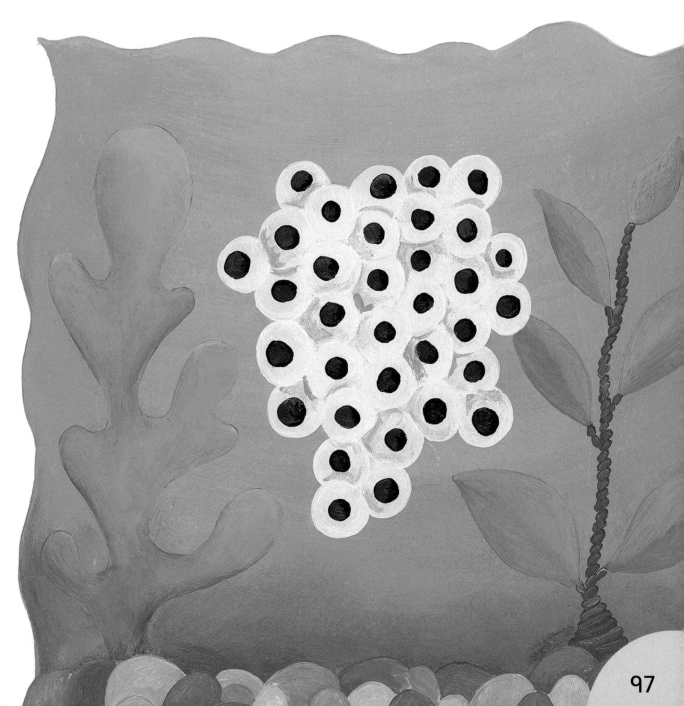

97

The dots are growing tails. They are baby tadpoles!

The tadpoles are tiny. They stick to the weeds.

# Then they begin to swim.

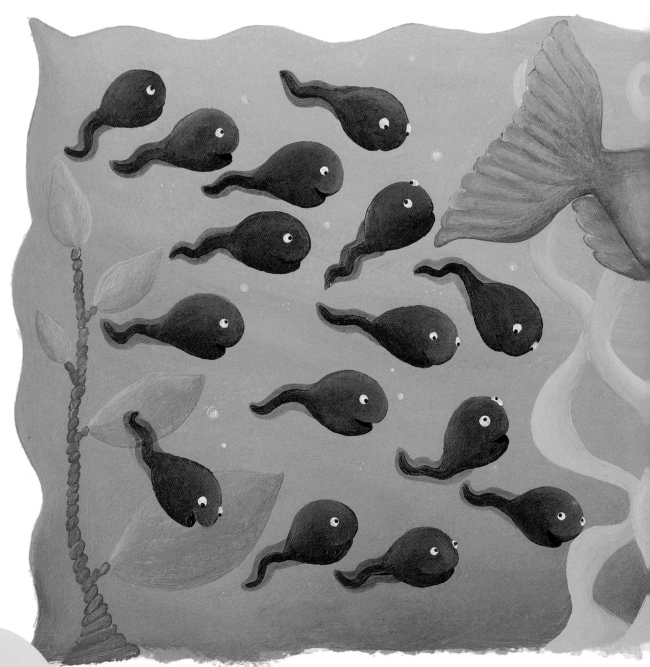

Quick, tadpoles, swim away!
Here comes a big fish!

The fish eats some of the tadpoles.

The rest swim away. They hide in the weeds.

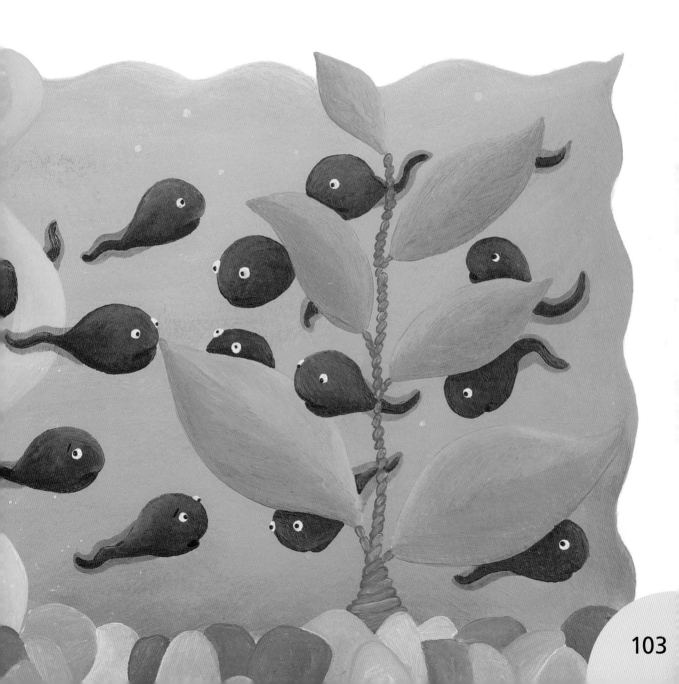

Can you see some bumps on this tadpole? Those bumps will be legs.

These tadpoles only have
back legs.

This tadpole has all its legs.
Its tail is shrinking.

This tadpole has no tail.

The tadpole kicks with its legs.
It jumps out of the lake.

But is it a tadpole?

No, it's a frog!

# Practise Your Phonics With
# Julia Donaldson's
# Songbirds

By the Author of The Gruffalo

## Look out for the other titles in the series …

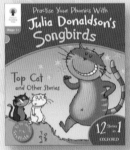

Top Cat and Other Stories
978-0-19-279296-9

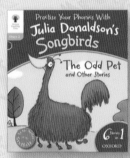

The Odd Pet and Other Stories
978-0-19-279297-6

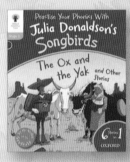

The Ox and the Yak and Other Stories
978-0-19-279298-3

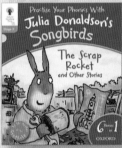

Scrap Rocket and Other Stories
978-0-19-279299-0

Where is the Snail? and Other Stories
978-0-19-279300-3

Tadpoles and Other Stories
978-0-19-279301-0

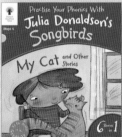

My Cat and Other Stories
978-0-19-279302-7

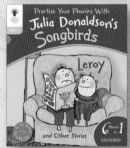

Leroy and Other Stories
978-0-19-279303-4

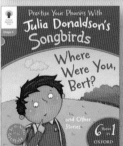

Where Were You Bert? and Other Stories
978-0-19-279304-1